Y0-COT-490

THE
·AFRICAN
ENVIRONMENT
PORTRAIT OF A CONTINENT

BY

Mary Louise Clifford
Edward S. Ross

NOBLE AND NOBLE, PUBLISHERS, INC.

NEW YORK · CHICAGO · DALLAS · LOS ANGELES · TORONTO

MARY LOUISE CLIFFORD has published books on Afghanistan, Malaysia and Liberia, as well as a novel on Burundi. A former member of th United States Foreign Service, she has spent five years living, traveling and writing in Africa. Her husband, whose advice and help have bee essential in developing this program, has been an economic adviser t three African governments under the United Nations Developme Program.

EDWARD S. ROSS, whose color photographs are used to illustrate this series, is a noted photographer, entomologist, and professor at the California Academy of Sciences who specializes in the study of tropical environments. He has been awarded a Guggenheim Fellowship in photography and his work has been published in encyclopedias, professional journals, and major popular and scientific magazines.

COVER: Near a lake in the Great Rift zone. Although such splendid specimens of wildlife still remain, much of Africa's animal population has been destroyed.

Contents

The Climate Belts of Africa

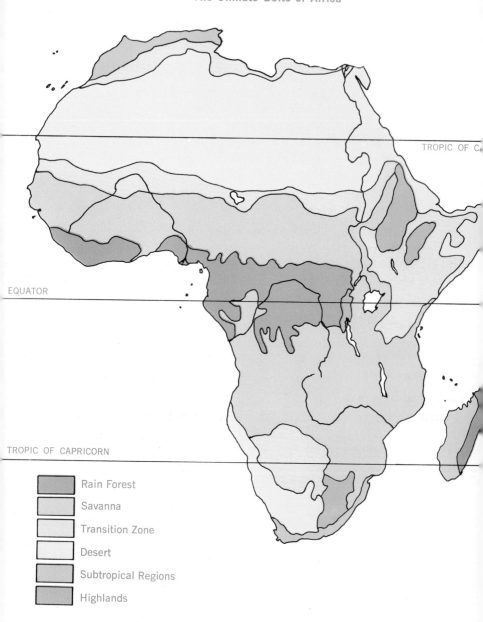

TROPIC OF C.

EQUATOR

TROPIC OF CAPRICORN

Rain Forest
Savanna
Transition Zone
Desert
Subtropical Regions
Highlands

The source streams of the world's largest river, the Nile, are found in the heart of the African continent. These streams flow through Lake Victoria, one of the largest lakes in the world. Not far from Lake Victoria, almost astride the Equator, mountains rise so high that they are crowned with snow throughout the year.

The world's greatest desert, the Sahara, spreads across the northern half of the African continent. Yet, in the equatorial forests of the Congo River basin, rainfall in places reaches three hundred inches a year.

Africa is the world's second largest continent, exceeded in size only by Asia. It is a continent of enormous diversity, with almost every sort of physical feature, climate, and plant and animal life imaginable.

A CONTINENTAL PATTERN

Although the climate zones of Africa are many and varied, they form a pattern of east-west climate belts that is easy to see on a map. These belts reflect the differences in rainfall that exist because of distances from the Equator. Africa extends about equal distances north and south of the tropics of Cancer and Capricorn; no other large land mass in the world sits so squarely on the

Sand dunes in the Namib Desert of
South-West Africa.

A turbulent stream in the rain forest
of Cameroon.

Equator. It is Africa's position on the Equator that causes climate belts that are similar both for the northern and southern halves of the continent.

THE RAIN FORESTS

At the center of Africa, astride the Equator, is a three thousand-mile belt of dense rain forest. Such forests are found on equatorial land throughout the world. Rain forests only grow in hot climates where rainfall is extremely heavy and is distributed evenly throughout all the months of the year. The principal mass of the African forest stands in the basin of the Congo River, but a narrow strip stretches west to the point where the great coastal bulge of the continent turns north.

The rain forest belt does not extend all the way to the east coast of Africa. It is interrupted by a unique feature of the African land mass: the Great Rift. This very unusual geological formation bisects Africa north to south, from Ethiopia to Mozambique. The Rift consists of massive volcanic highlands bordering a deep trough where the earth lies much lower than the surrounding peaks. Since the volcanic highlands do not have the rainfall or the deep soil that is essential for the lush vegetation and great tall trees of the rain forest, the rain forest ends where the Rift zone begins.

A Tropical World

It is easy to move about among the tall trees of the rain forest because the ground is covered only with mosses and low plants. The forest itself grows in several layers. At a level slightly above that of a man's head, masses of enormous ferns and creepers form the lowest layer. Often these tangled plants grow very densely. Above them are shrubs and small trees, also sometimes very dense, in a layer known as the understory. Up through the ferns and small trees grow the soaring, fluted trunks of the great trees. The trunks may reach a hundred feet or more before their massive crowns spread out to form the highest layer, the canopy of the forest. At ground level, the trunks of these trees form fluted buttresses in order to support their great height. Most of the trees are broad-leaved evergreens of an extraordinary variety of species all mixed together.

The canopy of the rain forest is high and thick and little sunlight penetrates, so the light on the forest floor is too dim for grass to grow. It is silent, too, in the rain forest, for the canopy is so high that the wind in the treetops cannot be heard on the ground. Only the animals break the silence.

A rain forest cannot support animals that graze on the ground. Here browsing and climbing animals thrive—monkeys (gorillas and chimpanzees) and apes in abundance, antelopes, okapi, bongo, bushbuck duiker, forest hogs and bush pigs, elephant and buffalo, leopards, and such oddities as tree pangolin, potto, and flying squirrels.

Man has cut away patches of the rain forest for his farm plots and houses, and human communities are scattered throughout the area. However, it has never been easy to move about in the forest, except by foot on narrow paths, which must constantly be cut and kept open. Frequent, heavy rainfall makes roads difficult to build and maintain. Rivers have never provided natural highways because the drop from the interior African plateau to the coastal plain causes rapids and waterfalls.

The edge of the rain forest has a natural boundary of low trees and dense shrubs. When man cuts away the high trees, this low, dense, tangled secondary jungle replaces them unless the land is kept constantly cleared. Once they are cut, the tall trees will take a very long period of time to grow again. The rain forest is gradually diminishing because of man's requirements for farming and grazing land.

The understory of the rain forest.

A game warden in Tanzania stands by the
buttressed trunk of a young forest tree.

Deep in the rain forest
of West Africa.

THE SAVANNAS

North and south of the equatorial rain forest are belts of wooded grasslands called savannas. The savannas begin at about 10° latitude on either side of the Equator and extend from coast to coast across the African continent. Rainfall on the savanna is plentiful—between forty and sixty inches a year—but falls only in one clearly defined season. The rainy season alternates with a dry season, which occurs during the other half of the year. The rains begin with the equinoxes—in June north of of the Equator and in December south of the Equator.

The big evergreen trees found in the rain forests cannot flourish through a dry season, so they are not found on the savannas. The trees of the savannas, however, can grow in the dry season, and during that season they drop their leaves, opening up the land below them to the sunlight. Tall grasses grow between the trees. The farther the distance from the Equator, the less the quantity of rain that falls, so the trees decrease in size, allowing more and more grass to flourish.

In the dry season, winds blow over the savannas from bordering deserts. The parched grass is very susceptible to fire, and the men who inhabit the savannas use fire to clear farmland. Fire also destroys the woodland and increases the available grassland.

The savannas can support large populations of wild grazing animals—wildebeests, gnus, zebras, hartebeests, gazelles, waterbucks, impalas, kobs, duikers, elands. These herbivorous animals are preyed upon by carnivorous animals, such as lions, leopards, cheetahs, hyenas, and wild dogs.

The savannas also support domestic grazing animals. Man has taken over large areas of the African savannas for his flocks of cattle, goats, sheep, and camels, as well as for his fields of food grain. On the West African savanna, most wild game has been destroyed by hunting and agriculture, and only gazelles, wild

The African savanna in northern Cameroon.

boars, and a few giraffes are left. The only grazing land left for wild animals is land too poor or too infested by the tsetse fly for domestic animals. The tsetse fly carries a parasite that causes sleeping sickness in man and a fatal disease to domestic animals. Wild animals are either immune or very resistant to this disease.

The West African Savanna

The West African savanna is unusual because it contains two great flood plains. One spreads out around Lake Chad; the other lies in the Mali plains of the upper Niger River basin. The Mali plain is spread out over ten thousand square miles of Mali and is fed by rainwater from the forest belt of the Futa Jalon Highlands. This plain has become an important area for irrigated agriculture in the twentieth century. Long ago, before there were any written records, the upper Niger basin was the location of the large African empires whose economies were based on extensive trade with North Africa.

Charting the Course of the Niger. Although they had heard about it for a very long time from many sources, it took European mapmakers centuries to get a clear picture of the Niger Valley. The Niger River itself is first mentioned in the chronicles of ancient historians who referred to it as a western branch of the Nile. After the eleventh century, Arab records mentioned it but claimed that, unlike the Nile, the Niger flowed west. The early Arab records also gave it its modern name, from a Berber word, *n'eghirren,* meaning stream.

The Niger emerges from the Futa Jalon Highlands barely two hundred miles from the Atlantic Ocean. The rainfall on the interior side of the highlands forms many small streams, which flow together in the plains of Mali to become the Niger River. The river flows northeast across the entire savanna, to the very edge of the Sahara. The Niger probably terminated in the remote interior of the Sahara many centuries ago. Long ago a

Giraffes are among the few wild animals
left in the West African savanna.

great stream flowed southeast from a point near the Niger's end, eventually emptying into the Bight of Benin. Geological changes thousands of centuries ago merged this stream with the Niger. Now, where the Niger meets a rocky escarpment on the edge of the desert, it turns southeast to wend its leisurely way back across the entire belt of savanna to reach the Atlantic on the coast of Nigeria.

Although the Niger is navigable for long distances, rapids divide it into three unconnected parts. Many tribes live in the three regions of the river's basin: the Mandingo and Bambara on the upper Niger, the Dogon and Songhai and Hausa in the region of the great bend, the Nupe and Ibo and Yoruba on the lower Niger. These are the dominant peoples, but there are many others, each speaking a different language and occupying a certain area of land that they regard as belonging to their tribe. River people might pole their canoes up and down the stretch of navigable river near their homeland, but each tribe is very jealous of any trespassing on its territory and very wary of venturing too far afield.

The river tribes became more hostile toward each other after the great Songhai Empire disintegrated and its individual tribes began struggling with each other in a contest for power. The peoples of the savanna were militant Moslems with little curiosity about the pagan peoples living in the rain forest to the south. They did not want the coastal peoples to penetrate inland and disrupt their caravan trade north across the Sahara. These Moslem peoples were even more wary of strangers who might be engaged in the slave trade and looking for captives to sell. As the New World demand for slave labor grew, the slave-buying European merchants supplied arms and ammunition to the coastal tribes that collected slaves for them. Distrust became so widespread that the Africans were seldom eager to give either information or help to curious explorers.

Arab travelers who crossed the Sahara were familiar with the upper reaches of the Niger River, although they had no contact

Sunset on the Niger River, which flows through the
West African savanna. *Courtesy of Robert L. Clifford.*

with or information about the river below its great bend. Leo Africanus, a famous traveler who wrote his records in about 1500, actually sailed about five hundred miles along the Niger River and should have known in what direction he was going. Yet, his chronicles state that the river flowed west, and European geographers showed it that way on their maps. A famous 1570 map, which has been preserved, erroneously shows the Niger flowing into the Senegal River, which empties into the West Atlantic. This mistake persisted until the end of the eighteenth century. Not until 1795 did an intrepid Scots doctor, Mungo Park, start on a tortuous journey inland from the Atlantic in search of the river's true course. During his seven-month exploration, Park endured severe bouts of malaria, hunger, and thirst; he lost his servants and interpreters and was even held captive by hostile tribes. He was too exhausted to embark on the river, but Park did determine that the direction of the river's flow was to the east.

Park returned to Africa nine years later, in 1805, intending to follow the Niger to its mouth, but his expedition never returned nor did it reach its destination. Some months after Park's departure, one of his servants followed Park's trail and found that the entire party had drowned. The actual location of the river's outlet remained unknown.

There was still considerable speculation in Europe that the Niger might possibly be the upper Congo. Expeditions were sent to the Congo to establish this fact, obviously without success.

In 1830, Richard Lander, a servant of another English explorer, and his brother John set off in a canoe to chart the part of the Niger that Park had not lived to navigate. After a dangerous journey, the brothers at last reached the Niger delta. They had finally completed the mapping of the great river and had filled in the main gaps on the map of West Africa.

There are other large rivers that drain the West African savanna. The Niger's great tributary, the Benue, adds as much water to the Niger's flow as does the Niger itself. In the west, the Senegal flows into the Atlantic, whereas the Volta, Cavally, and many smaller streams flow into the Gulf of Guinea. The Niger and the Benue are the only important water transportation routes. None of the others are navigable for more than a few miles because of their steep descent through falls and rapids from the mountains of the Guinea Coast.

The East African and Southern Savannas

The savanna in East Africa was, until World War II, the home of the most spectacular concentrations of wild animals left on earth. These herds seemed inexhaustible and were slaughtered indiscriminately for meat to feed prisoners of war. Since the war, man has spread rapidly into formerly wild lands. Large areas have been taken over for raising domestic animals and for farming in the well-watered areas around Lake Victoria.

The need to protect the wild animals from complete extinction has only been realized recently. Protected reserves have been set aside in national game parks, but they do not seem to provide foolproof protection. The animals leave the parks, migrating long distances in search of food. Outside the parks, they may be killed for meat or for their skins. Ranches and farms hinder their movements, and ranchers and farmers put pressure on their governments to take more and more land from the game preserves to support increasing human populations.

The history of the East African savanna is not a history of great trading kingdoms, such as those of West Africa. However, trade has been carried on along the East African coast for centuries, first by Arabs, then by Europeans. The Arabs penetrated inland as far as Lake Tanganyika in search of trade goods and slaves. European interest was not focused on East Africa until well into the nineteenth century, when Europeans were led into the East African interior in search of the answer to a question of burning interest—the source of the mighty Nile River.

Weaver birds build their nests in a narrow-leafed
thorn tree of the savanna.

A herd of impalas grazes on the savanna during the semidry season.

The great savanna belt south of the Equator fills most of southern Tanzania, southern Congo, Angola, Zambia, Rhodesia, and Malawi. This southern savanna lies mostly on ancient, elevated inland plateaus. Since its soil is poor and its nutrients badly leached away by rain, the southern savanna has never supported more than a thin population. This belt has more woodland than the northern savanna because it has never had to support large numbers of domestic cattle. Man has slaughtered great numbers of the wild animals in these southern woodlands, both for meat and in an unsuccessful attempt to control the tsetse fly.

South of the Equator, many clear streams rise in mountainous areas, flow out onto the savanna plateau, and eventually join the Zambezi River. Their fall from the inland plateau to the coastal plain is more abrupt than around the rest of the continent. Victoria Falls, for example, drops 343 feet into a mile-wide fissure in the earth. The sharp descent of these streams made African rivers of little use to travelers and was largely responsible for keeping the African interior closed to outsiders for many centuries. But the vast number and size of falls and rapids provides Africa with an enormous potential for hydroelectric power.

THE TRANSITION ZONES: BETWEEN THE SAVANNA AND THE DESERT

To the north and south of the savannas are what might be called transition zones between the savannas and the deserts. Rainfall is scanty and irregular in these regions. The amount of rain may decrease to as little as five inches a year, but it is still sufficient to sustain plant life. During the seasons of rainfall, these transition zones are covered as far as the eye can see with grass, broken by occasional low trees and bushes. The semidesert plants

A cheetah in the Serengeti Game Park of Tanzania.

Waterbuck in the national park outside Nairobi, Kenya.

The Zambezi River drops 343 feet over Victoria Falls
into a fissure in the southern savanna.

growing here must have seeds that can lie dormant through seasons of drought, then germinate very quickly when a rainy season comes, and go to seed immediately to await the next rains. These plants provide lush grazing for animals during perhaps only two months of the year, but even when they dry out, they turn into standing hay on which animals can survive.

Unlike the broad-leaved trees of the savanna, the trees of these transition zones are small in size. Trees that can live between the savanna and the desert survive on a minimum of moisture, grow deep roots to tap underground water, and have narrow, feathery leaves, which they drop in the dry season. Acacia trees cover great areas and vary in size, depending on the amount of moisture available to them. Small acacia bushes along the desert's edge contrast with the majestic flat-topped acacia trees of the East African game parks.

The Transition Zone of East Africa

The highlands of Ethiopia force the transition zone into an irregular pattern in East Africa. The transition belt does not stretch straight across to the east coast; it circles south of this elevated area and spreads south over a transition area known as the African Horn, which extends to the coast. This large desert and semidesert area includes the Somalia and Danakil deserts, regions of such harsh climate that vegetation is very scanty. Animals wander into these deserts from the vast savanna zone of the southern part of the continent, for there is no rain forest in the eastern part of Africa to separate a northern and southern savanna region.

The Horn is the key breeding area for the desert locust. This insect pest invades sixty countries and strips away vegetation from the Atlantic to the Bay of Bengal, from the Caspian Sea to Tanzania. International agencies are keeping close watch now on the breeding grounds and movements of the locust. Whenever

Succulent aloes store water in their tissues. Animals can
survive on this water when water holes dry up.

The gemsbok of southern Africa may have inspired
the legend of the unicorn.

These fat trunked baobab trees with their scant
foliage survive in the dry savanna.

they start to swarm, the locusts are sprayed with insecticides in an attempt to control this dreaded pest.

Between the Ethiopian highlands and the Somalia Desert, the monotony of the arid bush country is broken by Lake Rudolph. The lake is surrounded by great expanses of lava desert strewn with loose, black boulders that resemble sponges. As harsh as the countryside is, numerous grazing animals roam over it—gazelles, oryx, zebras. Browsing animals, such as the giraffe, gerenuk, and dikdik, feed on the shrubs, low trees, and creepers.

Further south, the transition zone runs into the coastal belt of Kenya and Tanzania. This coastal belt is predominantly overgrown by thorn thickets, which are the favorite haunts of elephants, rhinos, giraffes, koodoo, impala, and many birds. The few Africans living here call this thornbush *nyika,* which means "wilderness." Thorny trees, euphorbia bushes that store water, and grotesque baobab trees with fat semisucculent trunks thrive in this eastern zone.

The elephants feed on the succulent, spiky plants of bayonet aloe, which provides some of the moisture they need. They also dig holes in the dry watercourses and wallow in the shallow ponds, encouraging ground water to seep in. Other animals benefit from this water supply, as well as from the paths that elephants break open from water hole to water hole.

The Southern Transition Zone

The transition zone south of the Equator in southern Angola, Botswana (formerly named Bechuanaland), and South Africa is called the bushveld. Rainfall here is too scant for farming, and the tsetse fly makes much of the bushveld unsuitable for domestic flocks. Wild animals are being preserved in Kruger National Park. Flora and fauna are much the same as in the savanna, which the bushveld borders, except that the thorny euphorbia trees so common in East Africa are rather rare here.

Stone-covered areas called "regs" in the Namib
Desert of South-West Africa.

Dune areas called "ergs" in the Namib Desert.

THE DESERTS

Desert zones are found all around the earth astride the Tropic of Cancer and the Tropic of Capricorn, between the tropical savannas and the temperate zones. Africa has two such desert regions—the Sahara in the north, and the Kalahari, Karroo, and Namib deserts in the south.

It is not easy to tell where the savanna transition zone ends and the desert begins, since both regions have very limited rainfall. One way to tell transition zones from true desert is by the changing vegetation. In the transition zone south of the Sahara grows a prickly weed commonly called *cram cram.* It is a tough, broad-leaved grass, very similar in appearance to American orchard grass, except that its short stalk is covered not with small seeds, but with tiny, sharp burrs, which are the *cram-crams.* These burrs are so effectively designed by nature to stick to anything they touch that they even hook tenaciously to the soles of bare feet. They get into the wrap-around skirts of the African women and the long robes of the African men. They cling to children's hair and sleeping mats, to blankets and the coats of animals. The almost invisible prickers, which are sharper than thistle thorns, are almost impossible to remove because they break off when fingers remove the burrs. Some botanists say that the desert begins where there is not enough rain for the *cram-cram* to grow.

The Sahara

The Sahara (from the Arabic word *sahra,* which means a dull, brown emptiness) stretches three thousand miles from the Atlantic Ocean to the Red Sea. It is part of an even larger desert area that stretches east across Arabia into India. Africa's share

A scrubby Sahara tree that is characteristic
of desert vegetation.

of this enormous dry area is a thousand miles from north to south and covers 3.5 million square miles.

The prevailing winds over the Sahara come from the northeast. They carry moisture, but there are no high mountain chains blocking the path of these winds to cause clouds to rise and condense into rain. Less than ten inches of rain fall annually in the Sahara, and in many places no rain may fall at all for several years on end. This small quantity of rainfall is totally inadequate to make up for the rapid evaporation caused by the direct rays of the sun.

This is not to say that there are no mountains in the Sahara. There are extensive, very rugged mountain areas, notably the Hoggar and Tibesti mountains, which reach eleven thousand feet, but they are not arranged in such a way as to form a barrier to moisture-laden winds.

There are not only wild, mountainous areas in the Sahara but also vast stone and gravel plains, where violent winds laden with grit have scoured the surfaces clear of every particle of loose sand and dirt. This sand and dirt piles up in other areas into expanses of great rolling dunes, such as those found in Eastern Libya. These dunes are famous throughout the world, although actually only one-seventh of the Sahara is covered by dunes.

There are names for the three main types of desert found in the Sahara. The huge expanses of sand dunes are called *ergs.* The flat plains covered with coarse gravel and stones are *regs,* and the upland plateaus surfaced with stones or rock and cut by extinct watercourses are called *hammadas.*

The extremes of heat and cold in the Sahara are almost beyond belief. The thermometer often drops more than 60° at night, and frost is not unusual in the Sahara mountains. Temperatures as high as 170° F. in the daytime have been recorded.

In the high regions of the desert, any rainfall either runs off at once or is evaporated on the scorching hot rocks. The runoff from the mountains ends up in the many closed rock basins that characterize the flat area of the Sahara. (The Nile is in the only open basin of this region that runs into the sea.) Rain that falls in flat, sandy areas sinks in, and once it has sunk in a foot, it cannot evaporate or run off any further. Sand also absorbs less heat than does rock so that animals and plants can exist in sandy areas, whereas they could not possibly survive in the desert mountains.

Great areas exist in the Sahara where there are no water sources at all. But fortunately there are spots in most deserts where permanent water can be had from springs or wells. These are called oases, and they are normally planted with date palms, which provide food for nomads and travelers. There are also temporary desert pools, called *dayas,* where subterranean rivers flow. The lives of men and grazing animals in the desert are completely dependent on these sources of water. The Sahara is a vast barrier between the Mediterranean coast and the savanna. It has never been easy to cross. Even the Nile cannot be used as a highway into the interior because it is broken by several cataracts. But the Sahara has never been impenetrable because caravans could follow several chains of oases across its great expanse.

In order to survive in the desert, plants have thorns as well as repulsive tastes and smells to discourage animals from eating them. Desert animals must either be types that do not drink or sweat (reptiles and lizards) or types that are sufficiently mobile to cover long distances between water holes. Addax, gazelle, desert sheep and goats, ibex, and many birds are found in the Sahara.

The camel, although it is not indigenous to the Sahara, has been invaluable as a beast of burden in crossing the desert because it stores in its tissues water and fat, on which it can survive for days at a time. The donkey does this to a lesser extent, although it cannot go as long as the camel without drinking. These animals make it possible for large bands of nomadic peoples to

An oasis in the Sahara supports palm trees.

A Bedouin woman of North Africa picks
dates in an oasis.

A Sahara herdsman with his camels.

live on the desert's fringe and move long distances through it in search of grass for grazing.

The Deserts of Southwest Africa

Part of southern Africa is desert for the same basic reason as is the Sahara—its latitude. Only the river courses of this region can support much vegetation. The easterly winds drop their rain on the Drakensberg Mountains before they reach the Karroo. Also, Africa is a much smaller land mass in the south, so the Namib, Kalahari, and Karroo deserts are not nearly as extensive as the Sahara. These deserts are also cooler, with long, crisp winters and occasional sharp frosts. The Namib in particular has very low rainfall and little vegetation. It borders the west coast of Africa, but the Antarctic current runs up this coast, and it is too cold to generate rain. Many fur seals and a few penguins are found along this coast.

The Kalahari is less hostile than the Namib. It is actually a sub-desert steppe with a fairly good cover of vegetation. There are no big areas of rock, and any rain that falls sinks into the sand and stays there. This is why the Bushmen who live in the Kalahari always carry a long straw to push down into the sand and suck up subsurface drinking water, for there is practically no surface water to be found.

However, the Kalahari does support both domestic flocks and large numbers of nomadic animals, which live on sappy plants that supply their water needs. The gemsbok and springbok are the most typical of these animals, but there are also wildebeest, eland, koodoo, and red hartebeest.

THE SUBTROPICAL REGIONS

On the extreme northern and southern ends of the African continent are found narrow belts of subtropical climate. This

Fields and forests in the Atlas Mountains of Morocco.

Cork oak trees of Morocco provide an
important export crop.

type of climate is found throughout the world bordering oceans, immediately north of the Tropic of Cancer, such as California, or south of the Tropic of Capricorn, such as the southern cape of Africa. These regions have cool moist winters, with snow on high mountains, mild wet springs when plants grow luxuriantly, and hot dry summers.

The Mediterranean Coast

In North Africa, this coastal strip, watered by Atlantic winds, commences at the western end of Morocco and continues along the Mediterranean east through Libya, dwindling away in Egypt. The Atlas Mountains in the northwest corner of the continent serve as enough of a barrier to winds off the Atlantic to cause moderate rainfall. The rainfall of their Mediterranean slopes is sufficient to produce a cultivable belt along the North African coast. The spine of the Atlas Mountains is the belt's southern limit.

Vegetation in the North African coastal belt is more akin to that of Europe than of Africa. Although rainfall is not heavy (twenty to twenty-five inches annually), this region is densely inhabited and intensely cultivated, and has been for centuries. Much of the river water comes from snow melting in the Atlas Mountains.

The hills and plains of the Mediterranean coast have long since been stripped of their forest cover. The only trees that remain are olive trees, which are cultivated today, and cork oak, which is allowed to grow wild on sandy soils unsuitable for cultivation. The cork bark is a valuable commercial product; it is usually thought of as coming from Spain, but the largest cork orchards in the world are in Morocco.

The Rif Hills behind the coast are badly eroded and subject to regular flooding because they have been denuded of tree cover. Only in the remote high Atlas are forests still growing.

The Cape of Good Hope

The subtropical region of the Cape, on the southern tip of Africa, is similar to the Mediterranean coast. Both these regions have mountain ranges formed by folding beds of old rocks in relatively recent movements of the earth's crust. These are the only young fold mountains in Africa. On the southern Cape, this folded mountain range causes winter season clouds from the Indian Ocean to rise, condense, and drop their moisture. The climate is mild and pleasant, with occasional strong winds. The Cape is covered with a dense shrubbery known as *maquis* or *macchia*. Between the mountain ranges are broad, flat valleys, which support well-cultivated farms, vineyards, and orchards.

THE UNIQUE REGIONS OF AFRICA

The Nile and Its Sources

Several important areas of Africa are exceptions to the general climatic pattern of the continent. The fertile, well-watered lower Nile Valley—the most heavily populated area in all of Africa—does not properly belong in either the Mediterranean or the Sahara climate belts. Its flow begins south of the Sahara, over two thousand miles from the Mediterranean in the very heart of East Africa.

Travel for long distances on the Nile itself is impossible, for it is broken in several places by rapids and waterfalls, called cataracts. The cataracts are not complete barriers, for travelers can maneuver around them on foot. But further up the river to the south, beyond Khartoum, where the Blue Nile and the White Nile join together, is a vast region of impenetrable swamp called the Sudd. The Sudd is choked with solid masses of papyrus, reeds,

Buffels Bay on the Cape of Good Hope, South Africa.

Modern Cairo. The fertility of the lower Nile Valley has contributed
to the growth of cities in that area since ancient times.

aquatic grasses, and water lilies. The high temperature and strong sunlight shining on the vast slow-moving sheets of water that accumulate in the low, flat valleys of the Sudd encourage mats of plant growth so thick and solid that some animals can walk on them, even though the mass is floating. In fact, the Nile lechwe has a special spreading hoof for just this purpose. Hippos, crocodiles, Nile monitors, and pythons thrive in this lush area, but the uncharted tangle is impossible for boats to cross unless a channel is broken open and kept open.

Exploring the Nile. For centuries, Europeans had no idea of the source of this great river that rose every spring and flooded the land on its banks with moisture and rich silt. Rainfall in Egypt is very slight, and yet, this treasure poured out of a vast unknown region, year after year, giving life to the land along the river and sustenance to the rapidly growing population living there. Africans knew about the source of the Nile, but they were not interested in exploring to find it.

They had many reasons for not wanting to explore. Indiscriminate exploration frequently offended the Africans' sense of propriety. Each tribe had its own lands, and the tribal codes contained strong prohibitions against casual trespass into the area claimed by another tribe. The adult male African, particularly if he was a member of the warrior class, had an obligation to defend his tribal lands and automatically assumed that unidentified strangers were either rustling cattle or hunting for slaves. The Africans regarded wandering around outside their own territory as a sure way of asking for trouble. Some of them were willing to work for hire as porters and guides for explorers, and a few proved to be loyal beyond all expectations. David Livingstone walked all the way across the African continent, in spite of extreme ill health, to return his porters to the country in which he had hired them. When he died in the remote interior, it was two Africans who carried his body and his bundles of notes back to a European settlement, preserving priceless records that could just as easily have been abandoned in the jungle.

Other Africans agreed only very reluctantly to accompany the early European explorers. They knew perfectly well the hostility of tribes that would be encountered and the physical hazards of trying to sail down uncharted rivers and hack through swamps laden with mosquitoes and carrying the dreaded malaria virus.

Moreover, the Africans could not trust the motives of these strangers who seemed to have an insatiable appetite for information. The slave traders on the eastern coast had for many decades been sowing the seeds of distrust. Faced with the fear that these new white strangers from Europe might also have some idea of conquering and enslaving them, the Africans resorted to the attitude that has always served them best in dealing with strangers —politeness combined with extreme reticence in disclosing information. More often than not, the foreign explorers were on their own.

The geographer Ptolemy, who lived in Alexandria in the second century of the Christian era, wrote that the Nile flowed from two lakes fed by melting snows of the Mountains of the Moon. This information was surprisingly accurate, but no one outside of Africa believed it.

The Europeans doubted what they heard from the Africans about the source of the Nile. Their skepticism stemmed from the fact that Africa south of the Sahara was populated by hundreds of different tribes, speaking nearly eight hundred different dialects. None of these languages had written scripts so that the Africans were not equipped to draw maps of what they knew about their own continent. Cartography and geography were alien concepts to them. They had their own names for rivers and mountains and lakes, and the name was different in each language. When traders and explorers asked what was beyond the horizon, each tribe would tell them something different, and neither the Europeans nor the Africans recognized different names for the same thing.

Flamingos make their home on the alkaline
lakes of the Great Rift Valley.

Lake Victoria, source of the White Nile.

The Great Rift Valley traverses
the African continent from
the Red Sea to Mozambique.

A dozen tireless European explorers were to search through Africa for more than a century for the precise information that would enable them to draw the entire course of the Nile on the map.

Finding the Source of the Nile. In 1768, a Scotsman named James Bruce left Cairo with the express purpose of exactly locating the source of the Blue Nile. He entered the Ethiopian highlands from the Red Sea, reached Lake Tana, and followed the course of the river that flowed from the lake downstream to where it joined the White Nile. One part of the map had at last been correctly filled in, but the other mighty stream that fed the lower Nile was still a mystery.

In 1856, two Englishmen, John Hanning Speke and Richard Burton, traveled as far into the interior as Lake Tanganyika. Speke went on to Lake Victoria, which he named after England's queen. Speke was certain that the streams feeding the lake were the sources of the White Nile, but his claim was not to be proved correct for over fifteen years.

Mapping Central Africa. Other explorations did much to prove that Speke had indeed found the source of the Nile, but for many years there was still some question, since what lay south of Lake Albert and Lake Victoria remained unknown.

In 1865, David Livingstone led an expedition to map out the area between the Zambezi River and Lake Albert. He was heard from only twice during the next four years.

To Livingstone's astonishment, in November, 1871, a well-equipped column of porters appeared at his campsite on Lake Tanganyika headed by Henry Morton Stanley, who had been sent by the *New York Herald* to find the missing explorer. Livingstone and Stanley explored further, then parted company at Tabora. Livingstone waited there while Stanley outfitted another expedition in Zanzibar and sent it to him. Then Livingstone, still searching for the source of the Nile, turned south to find the

Mount Kilimanjaro in northern Tanzania, which the Africans call "God's throne."

course of the Lualaba River. He died in 1873 without achieving his goal of completing the map of Central Africa, but he had given Stanley enough information to finish the task.

Stanley returned to Africa in 1874. He reached Lake Victoria and sailed around its circumference, proving that the lake had only one exit—the Nile. Speke's belief that the Nile began with the streams feeding Lake Victoria was confirmed.

Stanley also explored Lake Tanganyika and determined that it had no connection with the Nile river system. His final accomplishment was to chart the course of the Congo River. With the completion of Stanley's explorations, the map of Central Africa was no longer blank.

The Great Rift Valley

These intrepid European explorers had charted large sections of the Great Rift Valley, one of the most striking geological formations in the world. The result of movements or fractures in the earth's crust, rather than of erosion or weathering, the Rift Valley is a huge trough slicing through the African continent. Actually its northern end is in the Beka Valley of Lebanon, while its southern formations are in Mozambique, at least those that are visible. The further extensions of the Rift are under the sea in the Mozambique Channel.

The geological activity that ultimately resulted in the formation of the Rift has occurred over a period of from 12 to 15 million years and is not finished yet. Even today, volcanoes between Lake Kivu and Lake Edward are evidence of continuing activity below the earth's surface.

Several extinct volcanoes stand in isolation on the East African plain. Two of them, Mount Kilimanjaro and Mount Kenya, are of unusual height and are crowned with snow throughout the year. When these two volcanic peaks were described by the first Portuguese missionaries who saw them, no one in Europe could believe that there were snowcapped mountains on the Equator.

Another group of snowtopped mountains in the Rift—the Ruwenzori—are not volcanic. They were thrust up by counter-movements of the earth's crust at the time the Rift Valley was formed. These movements were comparatively recent, perhaps 2 million years ago, and the Ruwenzori have been eroding rather quickly (as geological time is reckoned) ever since.

The Ruwenzori were the legendary "Mountains of the Moon," whose snows did indeed feed the lakes that the geographer Ptolemy had heard were the sources of the Nile. Because of their height, the moisture that condenses around their peaks, and the intense sunlight on the Equator, all these high mountains of Central Africa bear on their heights some extraordinary vegetation. Several distinct climate belts with differing vegetation extend around the Ruwenzori. Their bases are wrapped in rain forest. The next level is a coniferous forest, inhabited by elephants, buffalo, and rhino. Then there is a belt of mountain bamboo. Finally, below the snow line lies a girdle of mooreland. At this level, lichens and heath grow to incredible size, and giant groundsels and lobelias resembling exotic rock garden plants provide a landscape that might be imagined as the surface of another planet.

In addition to volcanoes and lakes, the Great Rift Valley is famous for hot springs, alkaline lakes, and flamingos. The alkaline lakes are caused by the diminution of water levels on lava soils; this diminution is due to evaporation by the scorching sun. The lakes in Kenya and to the south have been shrinking steadily since prehistoric times. The mineral content of the water becomes more concentrated and sodium salts increase until the water is so bitter that animals cannot drink it. Such increasing alkalinity is lethal to fish and to grazing or browsing animals. But the rapidly increasing algae life of such lakes is ideal food for flamingos, which sieve or filter the algae from the water without swallowing it. In fact, half of all the world's flamingos live in the Rift Valley.

Fossil remains found in the Rift Valley indicate that its floor

The snow-crested Ruwenzori Mountains
stand almost on the Equator.

The highlands of central Ethiopia.

was not always as harsh and dry as it is today. Anthropologists and archeologists digging at Olorgesaile and in the Olduvai Gorge near the Kenya-Tanzania border have found remains of much more extensive fauna than now lives in the valley. The whole area must have been dotted with lakes and swamps just before earliest man appeared there nearly 2 million years ago.

The Ethiopian Highlands

The Ethiopian highlands are not really a mountain range but a huge plateau that includes ranges of higher peaks and many isolated extinct volcanoes. Winds from the Indian Ocean blow across this highland area; these winds are laden with moisture that condenses into rainfall as the clouds rise to blow over the mountains.

Rainfall has for centuries been wearing away valleys in the soft, volcanic soil of the Ethiopian plateau, washing rich silt down into the Nile basin. Erosion has caused this soft rock to wash away into great gullies, leaving many rugged, flat-topped hills called *ambas*. For example, the Blue Nile below Lake Tana drops six thousand feet in only 400 twisting miles and has worn a tremendous gorge into which the whole Grand Canyon of the United States could be fitted without any difficulty.

The Ethiopian highlands must long ago have been covered with forests through which wild animals roamed in abundance. However, no region of Africa has been more brutally ravaged by man. The forests are almost completely cleared away. Man's misuse of the land has greatly speeded the natural erosion, and little vegetation blankets these convoluted hillsides. Great stretches of acacia scrub stand in mute contrast to man's cultivated plains in the valleys.

The South African Highlands

There are still other highlands in Africa. The interior of southern Africa is shaped much like a basin with raised edges, and the

Kalahari and Karroo desert regions lie in the bowl of this basin. The rim around it is known as the Great Escarpment. In parts of the Republic of South Africa, the escarpment rises to magnificent peaks in the Drakensberg Mountains, which are high enough to have snow in the winter.

West of the escarpment, a broad, flat plateau slopes gradually down into the Kalahari Desert. This grassland, called the "highveld," has always supported enormous herds of wild animals. However, great slaughter has thinned them out. Some animals— like the white-tailed gnu and the blesbok—are now extinct. No predatory animals are left, for the farmers will not tolerate them.

Madagascar

The island of Madagascar, fourth largest island in the world, was probably thrust apart from the mainland of Africa about 20 million years ago, during the same tremendous cataclysm that formed the Great Rift. Inhabited for perhaps less than two thousand years, its people are a true mixture of Asian and African blood, for many of the original settlers were Malays from Southeast Asia.

Long separated from the mainland by a channel two hundred and fifty miles wide, Madagascar does not have the later types of mammals common to the African continent. However, some very ancient forms of life persist there, notably a whole group of lemurs and some primitive species of fish. The little tenrec is the island's most primitive mammal.

Madagascar was also the home of an extraordinary gigantic bird that laid eggs as big as footballs. Although never actually seen by reliable witnesses, this bird was described by Marco Polo as the "gryphon bird," and Sinbad the Sailor in *A Thousand and One Nights* claimed to have seen the "fabled roc, or rukh." Intact eggs and nearly complete skeletons of this ostrich-like bird, *Aepyornis,* have been found that reveal it to have been almost ten feet high and to have weighed close to a thousand pounds. Like

The Cape Nature Reserve in South Africa.

today's ostrich, this giant bird was unable to fly, and it must have become extinct fairly recently.

Live coral has built up extensive reefs around both Madagascar and the Comoro Islands, which lie just to the northwest. But along the western coast of the African mainland, the cold water of the Antarctic current prevents the formation of coral.

GUARDING A HERITAGE

In the 2 million years since man first evolved in Africa, the human species has taken an enormous toll in vegetation and wild animal life. Pressures have mounted particularly in the last century, during which the introduction of modern medicine by the colonial powers resulted in a very rapid increase in population.

On Madagascar alone, man has cleared away almost three-quarters of the island's natural vegetation, and exotic animal life that existed until very recently has become extinct. The Ethiopian highlands have also been stripped of much of their natural vegetation, destruction that correlates directly with the density of human population and the length of time man has lived there.

The Great Escarpment of the Drakensberg Mountains in South Africa has been so stripped of its trees and plants that the Kenyan naturalist Leslie Brown calls the escarpment "a ruined paradise." In the grasslands of Natal, the only wild animals left are those that settled farmers know will not destroy their crops. The same is true on the Mediterranean coast of North Africa.

In the grasslands of the savannas and transition zones, plant cover has in many places been so overgrazed by domestic flocks that it is no longer sufficient to sustain them. Wild animals, such as the impala and eland, could survive but would have to be actively encouraged to return to such barren haunts.

The realization is only now developing that the degree of destruction of grazing land depends very much on the combination of animals that are grazed. Cattle and sheep are the most destruc-

gger canoes of Malay style on the beach of an island
g village off the coast of Madagascar.

Slash-and-burn farming has destroyed much of
Africa's virgin forest.

tive grazers of all, for in semiarid country they eat away all the sweet grass so that only thorny bush is left. Goats are destructive browsers, chewing up shrubs as high as they can reach, but they are a natural compliment to cattle and sheep because they are less interested in grass.

The ideal combination for conserving the land seems to be a mixture of wild animals with the domestic—impala, eland, koodoo, and others of the same type which will eat the species of grasses and shrubs that domestic animals ignore. The grazing habits of wild animals are less destructive than those of domestic animals, for they move in looser groups. Moreover, wild animals do not overgraze in one place, as man so often forces his animals to do because he himself is reluctant to move. For most purposes, stocking wild game could be more productive than raising cattle, as has been done traditionally.

The settled farmers of the savanna burn off the woodlands to make room for their small fields. Only the fire-resistant species of plant life grow back—the thorny acacia and tamarinds, and the tall savanna grasses. The grasses, once dried out, ignite easily and burn fiercely, and great areas can be blackened by lightning or accident. Once the ground is denuded of its cover, the wind and rain trace the patterns of erosion that are so common to much of the continent.

Even the rain forest recedes slowly before man's never-ending needs. Once the great trees are felled, only thick, low jungle replaces them. As man continues to burn and hack away at this secondary growth, it deteriorates into savanna. When the trees and grass have given way to the millet fields and the roaming herds of cattle, there is little plant life left to hold the moisture. The forest recedes, and the desert creeps slowly into the grasslands. At the same time, because of his steadily increasing numbers, man demands more and more food of the land.

The abundance of Africa is not infinite. Its great variety of plant life, which ranges from the flat Sahara cauliflower to the soaring rain forest mahoganies, will not last forever in the face

of human destruction. The great herds of wild animals that so excite the imaginations of tourists and naturalists cannot survive without protection. Some of the most interesting areas of Africa are now protected by animal and forest preserves, but to this beginning step must be added enormous conservation efforts in the realm of domestic agriculture if the rich heritage that still exists in Africa today is to be preserved for future generations.

s, desperate for food, climb scrubby desert
to find green foliage to eat.

Glossary

alkaline: Containing soluble sodium or potassium salts.

amba: A flat-topped hill of the Ethiopian highlands produced by the erosion of soil into gullies around it.

Blue Nile: The branch of the Nile that flows from Lake Tana and merges with the White Nile at Khartoum.

bush: A sparsely populated region that supports some forest or scrub plant cover.

bushveld: A thinly settled grassland in southern Africa that supports some forest or scrub plant cover.

carnivorous: Flesh-eating.

coral: A tiny, cylindrical sea animal that lives in colonies and excretes a hard, skeletal substance, which accumulates to form reefs.

delta: A fertile area at the mouth of a river formed by the river's flood deposits, which generally break the river's mouth into several channels.

desert: Land where rainfall does not exceed five inches per year.

equinoxes: The two times during the year when the sun passes over the Equator and when day and night are equally long all over the earth.

erg: Desert with a surface of sand.

fauna: Animal life of a particular environment.

flood plain: A level area around a natural water source.

flora: Plant life of a particular environment.

folded mountains: A series of broad ridges in the earth's surface that are produced by movements of the earth's crust.

Great Escarpment: The mountainous rim between the interior plateau of southern Africa and the coastal plain.

Great Rift Valley: An immense volcanic trough extending from the Beka Valley in Lebanon south through Africa to Mozambique.

hammada: Desert with a rock-strewn surface.

headwater: The source of a stream or river.

herbivorous: Plant-eating.

indigenous: Originally produced or living in a specified environment.

latitude: Distance north or south of the Equator.

mooreland: Thinly populated, rolling land that is infertile and often marshy.

nomadic: Having no permanent living place.

plateau: A level area of land with a surface that stands above adjacent land on at least one side.

rain forest: A tropical woodland dominated by tall, broad-leaved evergreen trees that has extremely heavy annual rainfall distributed through every month of the year.

reg: Desert with a graveled surface.

savanna: A tropical or subtropical grassland scattered with deciduous trees, which has distinct wet and dry seasons.

steppe: Arid, level, unforested land covered with grasses that can survive without much moisture.

transition zone: Region with less rainfall than the savannas, but with greater and more regular rainfall than the deserts.

Tropic of Cancer: The parallel of latitude that lies 23½ ° north of the Equator.

Tropic of Capricorn: The parallel of latitude that lies 23½ ° south of the Equator.

tropics: The region that lies between the Tropic of Cancer and the Tropic of Capricorn.

White Nile: The branch of the Nile that flows from Lake Victoria and merges with the Blue Nile at Khartoum.

Suggested Readings

ADAMSON, JOY, *Born Free*. New York, Harcourt, Brace & World, Inc., 1960.

——. *Forever Free*. New York, Harcourt, Brace & World, Inc., 1963.

—— *Living Free*. New York, Harcourt, Brace & World, Inc., 1961.

ARUNDEL, JOCELYN, *The Wildlife of Africa*. New York, Hastings House, 1965. Grades 6–9.

BROWN, LESLIE, *Africa: A Natural History*. New York, Random House, Inc., 1965. Outstanding study of the geography, climate, and wildlife of Africa by a Kenyan naturalist. Excellent reading for young adults. Beautifully illustrated and mapped.

CARR, ARCHIE, *The Land and Wildlife of Africa*. New York, Time Inc. Book Division, 1964.

EATON, JEANETTE, *David Livingstone, Foe of Darkness*. New York, William Morrow and Company, Inc., 1947. Grades 7–11.

HALL-QUEST, OLGA W., *With Stanley in Africa*. New York, E. P. Dutton & Co., Inc., 1961. Grades 7–9.

McKOWN, ROBIN, *The Congo, River of Mystery*. New York, McGraw-Hill, Inc., 1968.

MOOREHEAD, ALAN, *No Room in the Ark*. New York, Harper & Row, Publishers, 1959.

——. *The Story of the Blue Nile*. New York, Harper & Row, Publishers, 1966. Grades 6–9.

——. *The White Nile*. New York, Harper & Row, Publishers, 1960. Adult.

STERLING, THOMAS, *Exploration of Africa*. New York, American Heritage Publishing Company, Inc., 1963. Grades 7 and up.

WILMERDING, WALTER J., *The Big Ones and Other Beasts*. New York, G. P. Putnam's Sons, 1966. A study of African animals.

Index